The Joy of Having Fun at the Piano

"Goodbye to care when you whistle the air
Of the song that you can't forget."
The poet Guy Wetmore Carryl feels as we do.
What is more fun than group singing?
Funny songs, tender and boisterous songs,
folk songs, love songs: Songs to warm the hearts
of any group gathered around the piano.
THE JOY OF HAVING FUN AT THE PIANO
presents some of America's favorites.

The piano arrangements by Denes Agay are simple;
first and second year students can play them with
ease. Their solid musical quality recommends them
as teaching material. Chord names have been included.

A few hints. Small, impromptu get-togethers are
the most fun. Singing in harmony should be
encouraged. Before large meetings a song
leader should rehearse with his accompanist.
Variety is the spice of life so select from the
various categories here and sing out.

Copyright © 1964, 1980 Yorktown Music Press, Inc.
All Rights Reserved

US ISBN 0.8256.8003.4
UK ISBN 0.7119.0324.7

Exclusive Distributors:
Music Sales Corporation
24 East 22nd Street, New York, NY 10010 USA
Music Sales Corporation
78 Newman Street, London W1P 3LA England
Music Sales Pty. Limited
27 Clarendon Street, Artarmon, Sydney NSW 2064 Australia

Printed in the United States of America by
Hamilton Printing Company
7/85

Contents

Amazing Grace

Folk Hymn

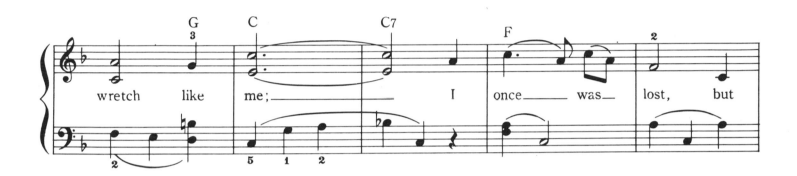

2. 'Twas grace that taught my heart to fear,
   And grace my fears relieved;
   How precious did that grace appear
   The hour I first believed.

3. Thro' many dangers toils and snares,
   I have already come;
   'Tis grace that bro't me safe thus far,
   And grace will lead me home.

4. How sweet the name of Jesus sounds
   In a believer's ear;
   It sooths his sorrows, heals his wounds,
   And drives away his fear.

5. Must Jesus bear the cross alone
   And all the world go free?
   No, there's a cross for ev'ry one
   And there's a cross for me.

Scarborough Fair

English – American Folk Song

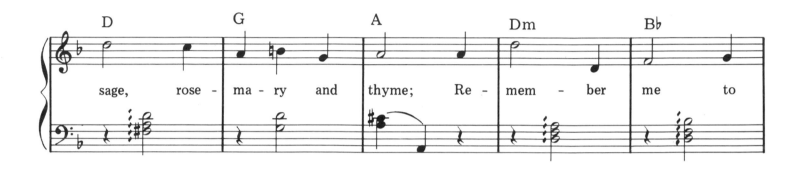

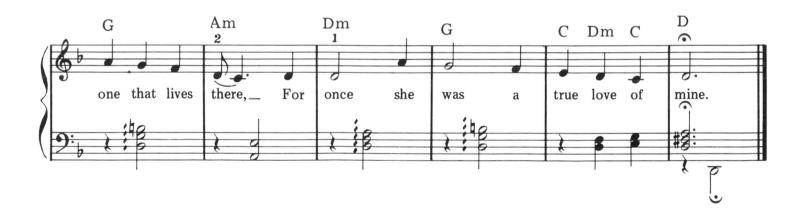

2. Tell her to make me a cambric shirt,
   Parsley, sage, rosemary and thyme;
   Without any seam or fine needlework,
   And then she'll be a true love of mine.

3. Tell her to wash it in yonder dry well,
   Parsley, sage, rosemary and thyme;
   Where water ne'er sprung, nor drop of rain fell,
   And then she'll be a true love of mine.

4. Oh, will you find me an acre of land,
   Parsley, sage, rosemary and thyme;
   Between the sea foam and the sea sand
   Or never be a true lover of mine.

5. Oh, will you plough it with a lamb's horn,
   Parsley, sage, rosemary and thyme;
   And sow it all over with one peppercorn,
   Or never be a true lover of mine.

6. Oh, will you reap it with a sickle of leather,
Parsley, sage, rosemary and thyme;
And tie it all up with a peacock's feather,
Or never be a true lover of mine.

7. And when you have done and finished your work,
Parsley, sage, rosemary and thyme;
Then come to me for your cambric shirt,
And you shall be a true love of mine.

Michael Row the Boat Ashore

Spiritual

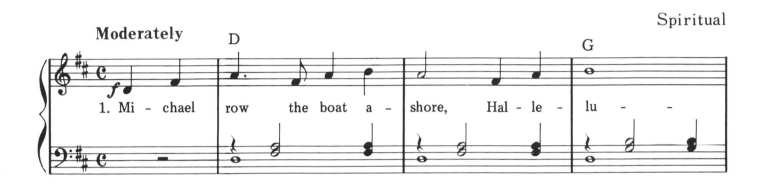

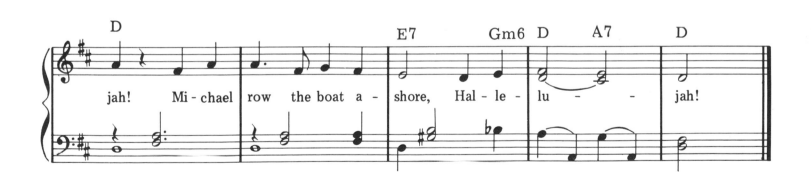

2. Brother, lend a helping hand, Hallelujah!
Brother, lend a helping hand, Hallelujah!

3. Sister, help to trim the sail, Hallelujah!
Sister, help to trim the sail, Hallelujah!

4. Jordan's River is deep and wide, Hallelujah!
Meet my mother on the other side, Hallelujah!

5. Jordan's River is chilly cold, Hallelujah!
Kills the body but not the soul, Hallelujah!

6. Trumpet sound the jubilee, Hallelujah!
Trumpet sound the jubilee, Hallelujah!

7. Michael, row the boat ashore, Hallelujah!
Michael, row the boat ashore, Hallelujah!

Aura Lee

George R. Poulton

Simply, tenderly

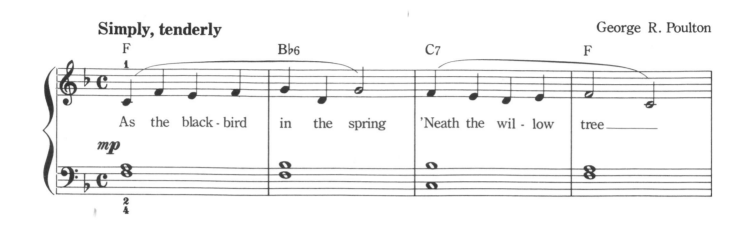

As the black-bird in the spring 'Neath the wil-low tree____

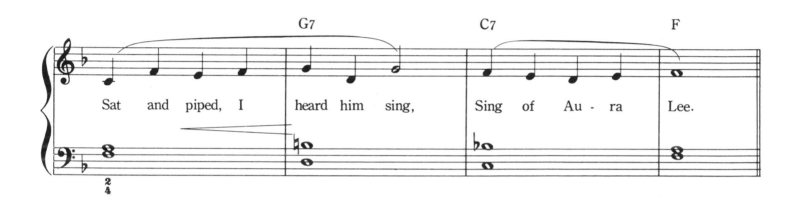

Sat and piped, I heard him sing, Sing of Au-ra Lee.

Chorus

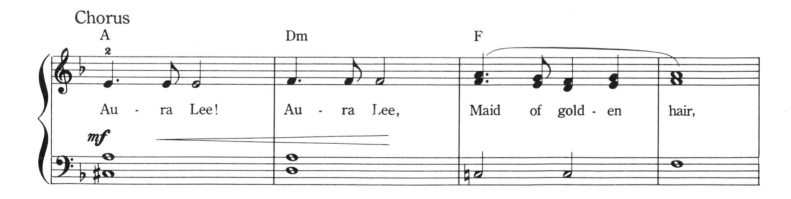

Au-ra Lee! Au-ra Lee, Maid of gold-en hair,

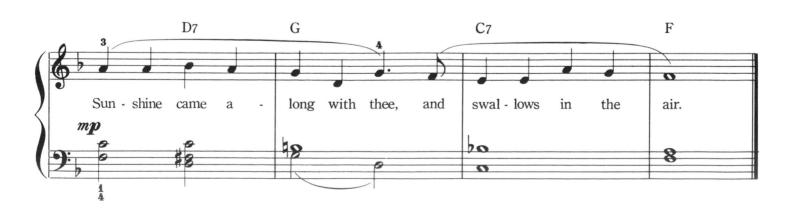

Sun-shine came a-long with thee, and swal-lows in the air.

In The Good Old Summer Time

Ren Shields

George Evans

Bill Bailey
(Won't You Please Come Home)

Bright cake-walk

Hughie Cannon

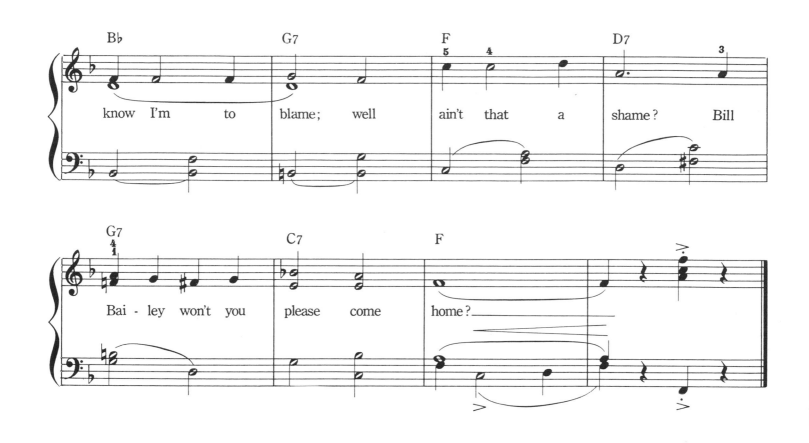

Row, Row, Row Your Boat
(Round)

Traditional

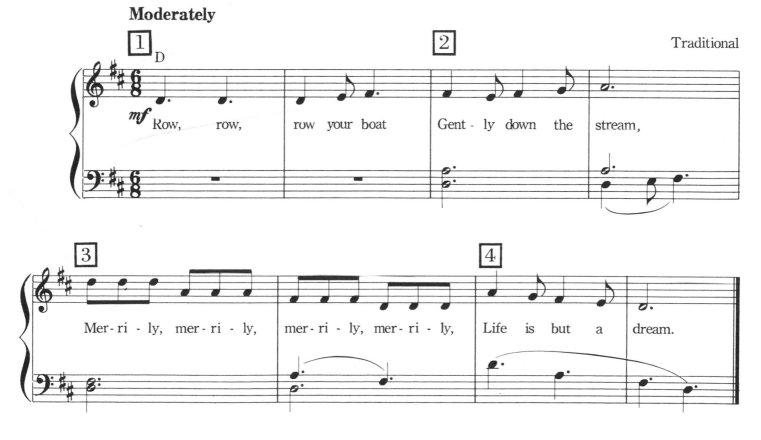

Kentucky Babe

Richard Henry Buck

Adam Geibel

Sleepy, lilting tempo

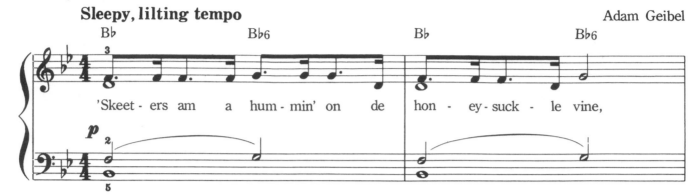

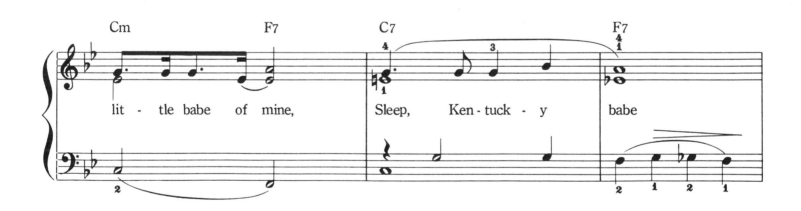

Meet Me In St. Louis, Louis

Andrew B. Sterling

Lively waltz

Kerry Mills

My Wild Irish Rose

Moderately

Chauncey Olcott

In The Shade Of The Old Apple Tree

Harry H. Williams

Slow waltz tempo

Egbert van Alstyne

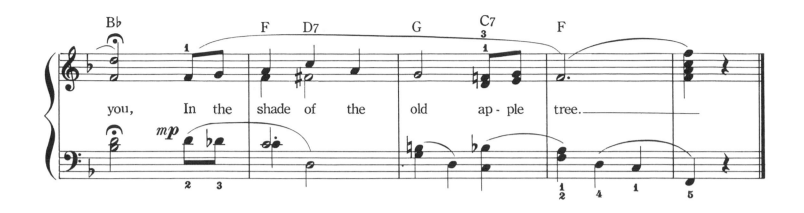

My Nelly's Blue Eyes

Moderate waltz

William J. Scanlon

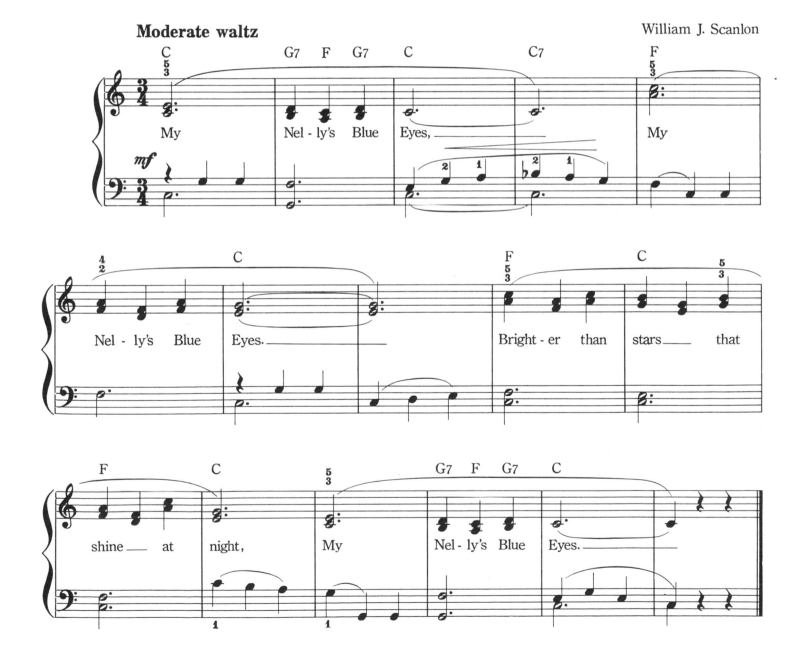

Goodbye, My Lady Love

Joseph E. Howard

Strutting

Good-bye my la - dy love,— Fare-well my tur - tle dove,—

You are the i - dol and dar - ling of my heart, But some day

You will come back to me,— And love me ten - der - ly,— So

good - bye, my la - dy love good - bye.—

Under The Bamboo Tree

Bob Cole

Rosamond Johnson

Yankee Doodle Dandy

George M. Cohan

I'm a Yan-kee Doo-dle Dan - dy, Yan - kee Doo-dle do or die; Real live neph-ew of my Un - cle Sam's, Born on the Forth of Ju - ly. Got a Yan-kee Doo-dle sweet - heart, She's my Yan-kee Doo-dle joy.

Sweetly Sings The Donkey
(Round)

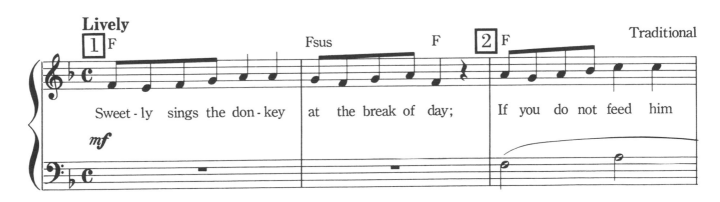

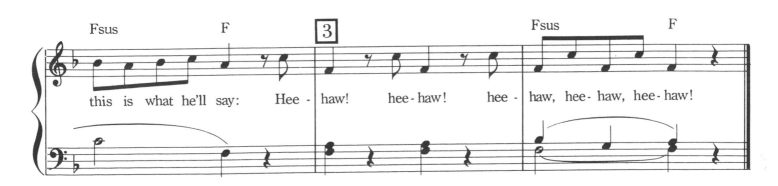

You're A Grand Old Flag

Lively march tempo

George M. Cohan

The Sidewalks Of New York

Charles B. Lawler

Lively waltz

James W. Blake

East side, West side, All a - round the town,

The tots sang "ring a ro - sie," "Lon - don Bridge is fall - ing

down." Boys and girls to - geth - er,

Me and Ma - mie O' Rorke, We tripped the light fan -

tas - tic On the side - walks of New York.

There Is A Tavern In The Town

Bright polka tempo

Traditional

Far Above Cayuga's Waters

C. K. Urguhart

H. S. Thompson

Mary's A Grand Old Name

George M. Cohan

The Man On The Flying Trapeze

Lively waltz

Traditional

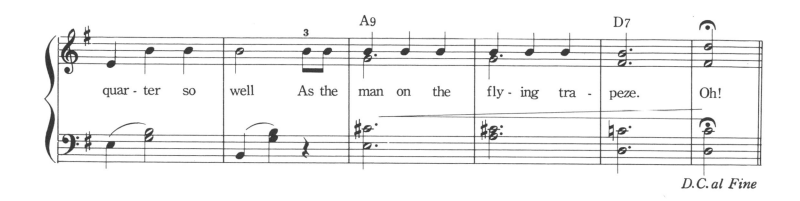

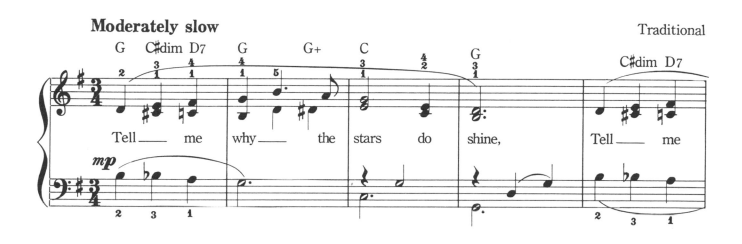

Tell Me Why

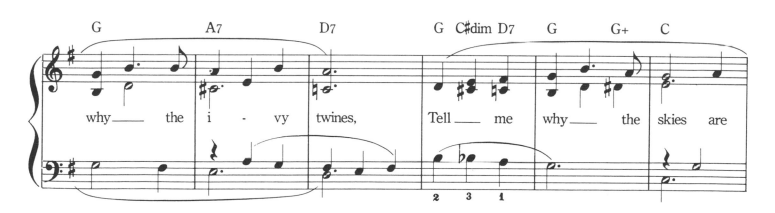

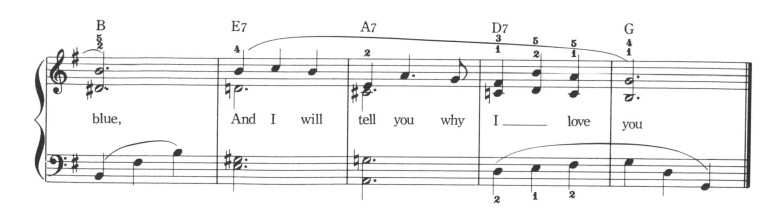

Love's Old Sweet Song

G. Clifton Bingham

James Lyman Molloy

The Sweetest Story Ever Told

R. M. Stults

Gypsy Love Song
(from " The Fortune Teller")

Harry B. Smith

Victor Herbert

Slowly

Slum - ber on, my lit - tle gyp - sy sweet-teart,
Dream of the field and the grove.____ Can you
hear me, hear me in that dream-land, where your fan - cies rove?____
____ Slum - ber on, my lit - tle gyp - sy sweet - heart,
Wild lit - tle wood - land dove;____ Can you

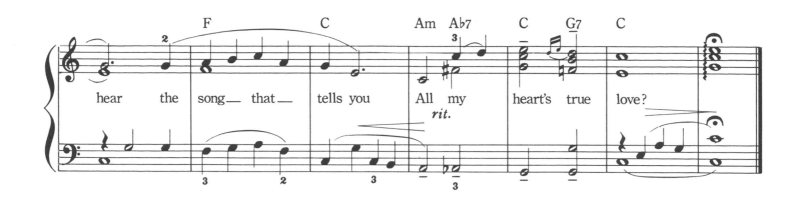

hear the song__ that__ tells you All my heart's true love?

The Bowery

Charles H. Hoyt

Percy Gaunt

Lively waltz

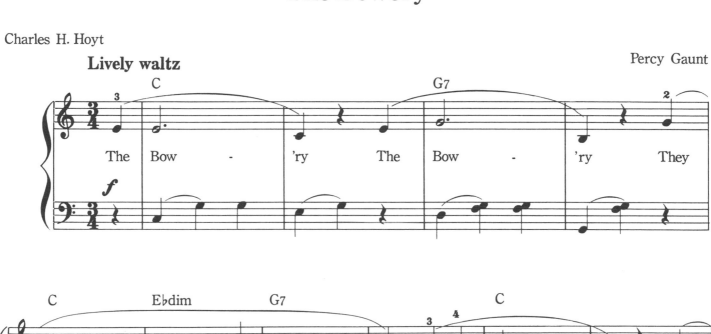

The Bow - 'ry The Bow - 'ry They

say such things and they do strange things, On The Bow - 'ry, The

Bow - 'ry, I'll nev - er go there an - y more.__

Kiss Me Again

from "Mlle. Modiste"

Music by Victor Herbert
Words by Henry Blossom

Slow waltz tempo

In The Evening By The Moonlight

James A. Bland

In The Gloaming

Meta Orred

Annie F. Harrison

think of me and love me As you did once long a - go?

Yale Boola

Spirited walking tempo

A.M. Hirsh

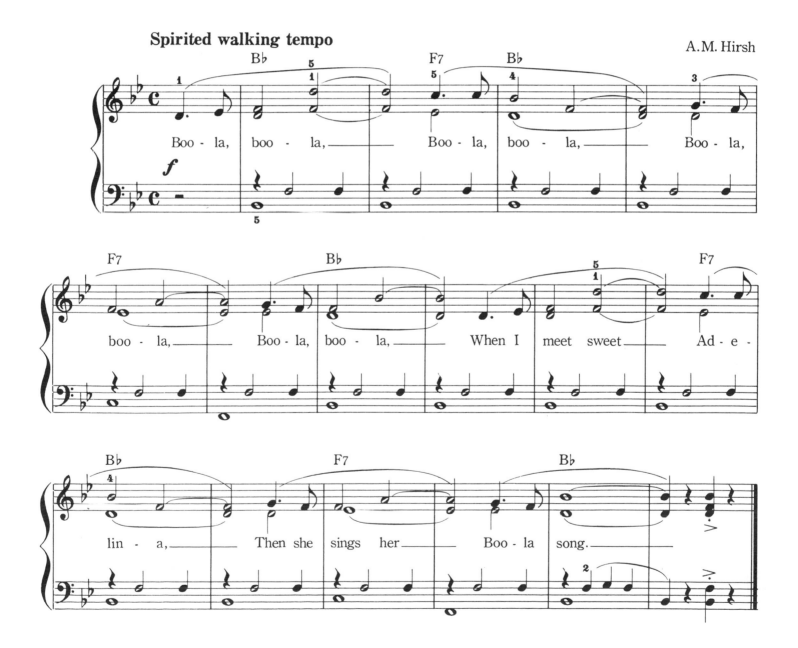

Boo - la, boo - la, ____ Boo - la, boo - la, ____ Boo - la,

boo - la, ____ Boo - la, boo - la, ____ When I meet sweet ____ Ad - e -

lin - a, ____ Then she sings her ____ Boo - la song. ____

Kashmiri Song

Laurence Hope

Amy Woodforde - Finden

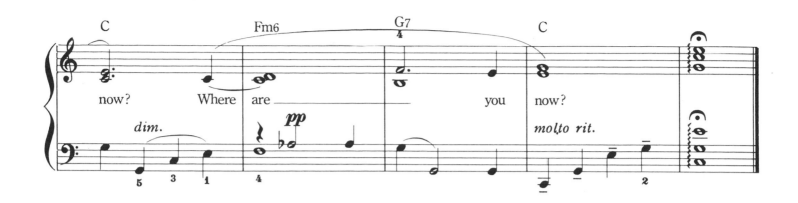

now? Where are _____ you now?

On The Banks Of The Wabash

Moderately slow

Paul Dresser

Oh, the moon-light's fair to-night a-long the Wa-bash, From the

fields there comes the breath of new mown hay; Thro' the syc-a-mores the can-dle-lights are

gleam-ing On the banks of the Wa-bash, far a-way.

I Have A Song To Sing, O!

(from "The Yeomen of the Guard")

William S. Gilbert

Arthur Sullivan

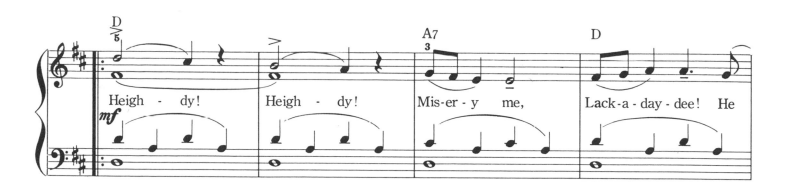

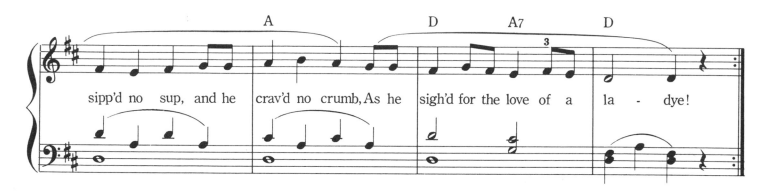

The Flowers That Bloom In The Spring

(from "The Mikado")

William S. Gilbert

Arthur Sullivan

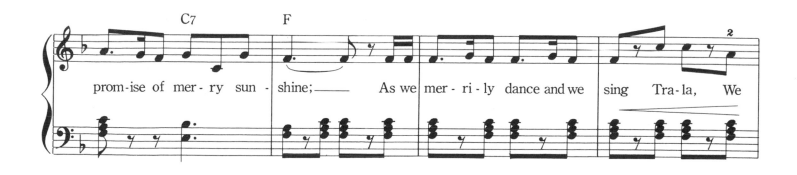

When I Was A Lad

(from "H.M.S. Pinafore")

William S. Gilbert

Arthur Sullivan

I Am The Very Model
(from "The Pirates Of Penzance")

William S. Gilbert

Arthur Sullivan

43

Oh Promise Me

Clement Scott

Reginald de Koven

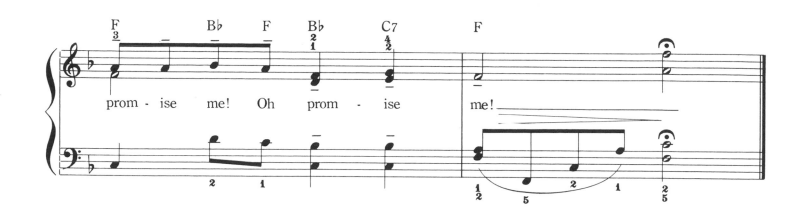

prom - ise me! Oh prom - ise me!

Lovely Evening

(Round)

Traditional

Moderately slow

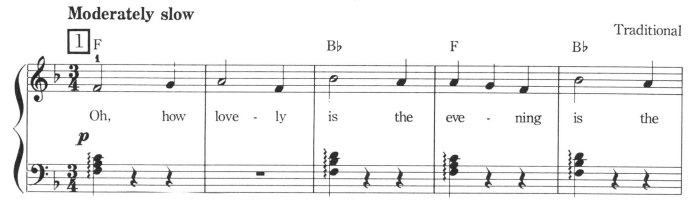

Oh, how love - ly is the eve - ning is the

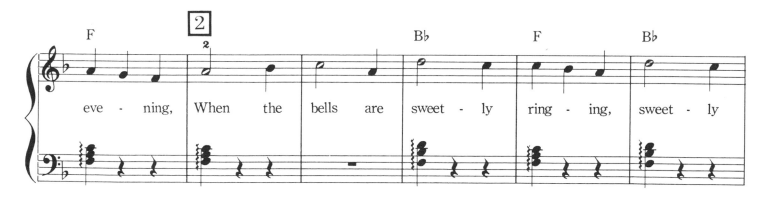

eve - ning, When the bells are sweet - ly ring - ing, sweet - ly

ring - ing Ding, dong, ding, dong, ding, dong!

Londonderry Air

Katherine Tynan Hinkson

Irish Song

While sun and shade your robe of lawn will dap - ple,

your robe of lawn,___ And your hair's___ spun___ gold.___

Ida! Sweet As Apple Cider

Eddie Leonard

Eddie Munson

Moderately lively

I - da!___ sweet as ap - ple ci - der,

Sweet - er___ than all I know,___

Short'nin' Bread

Traditional

The Rosary

Robert Cameron Rogers

Ethelbert Nevin

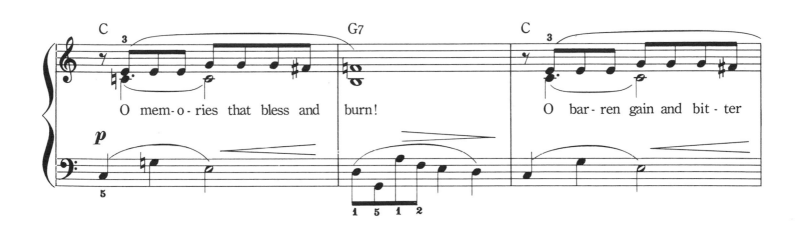

While Strolling Thru The Park

Ed Haley

Moderate walking tempo

med-i-ate-ly raised my hat, And made a po-lite re - mark; I

nev-er shall for-get the love-ly af-ter-noon I met her at the foun-tain in the park.

Carry Me Back To Old Virginny

Moderately slow

James A. Bland

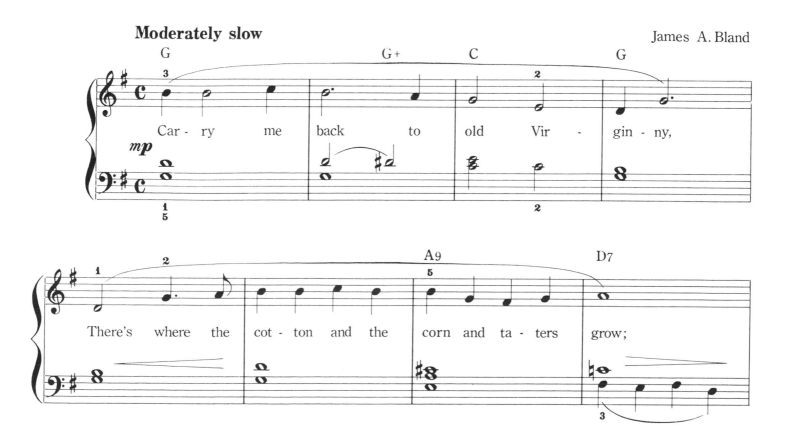

Car - ry me back to old Vir - gin - ny,

There's where the cot - ton and the corn and ta - ters grow;

My Bonnie

Because

Words by Edward Teschemacher

Music by Guy d'Hardelot

Freely moving

Be - cause you come to me with naught save love, And hold my hand and lift mine eyes a - bove, A wi - der world of hope and joy I see, Be - cause you come to me. Be - cause you speak to me in ac - cents sweet, I

Vilia

(from "The Merry Widow")

Ted Fetter

Franz Lehar

mine; If I could just make thee mine.

For He's A Jolly Good Fellow

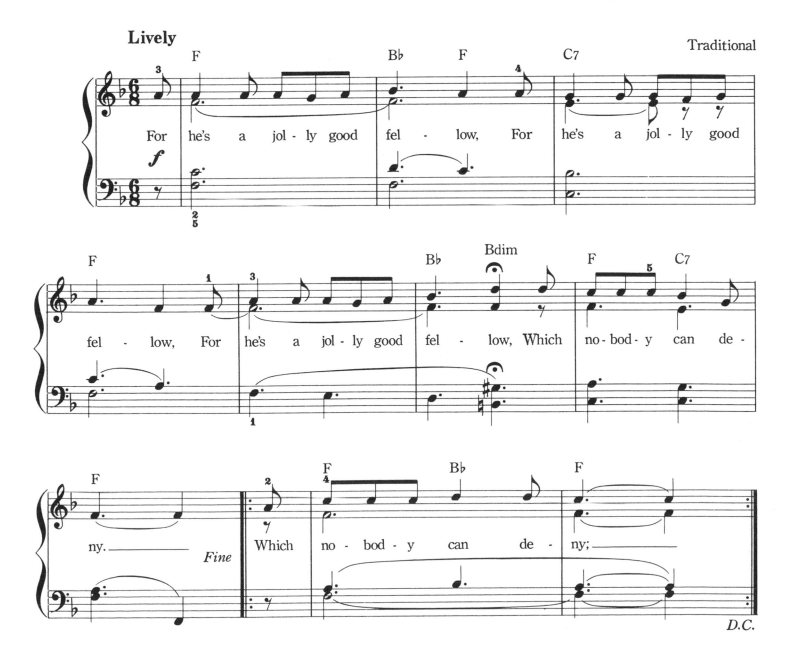

For he's a jol-ly good fel-low, For he's a jol-ly good

fel-low, For he's a jol-ly good fel-low, Which no-bod-y can de-

ny. _Fine_ Which no-bod-y can de-ny;

D.C.

She'll Be Comin' Round The Mountain

Traditional

She Wore A Yellow Ribbon

Bright

Traditional

'Round her neck she wore a yel - low rib - bon, She wore it in the win - ter and in the month of May; And when they asked her why on earth she wore it, She said "It's for my lov - er who is far, far a - way." Far a - way! Far a - way! Oh, she wore it for her lov - er who was far, far a - way.

Life In The Army

Moderately

Traditional

1. The bis-cuits in the ar-my they say are might-y fine, But one rolled off the ta-ble and killed a pal of mine; Oh, I have had e-nough of ar-my life, Gee, Ma, I wan-na go, Hey, Ma, I got to go, Gee, Ma, I wan-na go home.

2. The coffee in the army
   they say is might fine,
   It looks like mud and water
   and tastes like iodine;
   Oh, I have had enough of army life, etc.

3. The chicken in the army
   they say is might fine,
   But once two drumsticks got up
   and started beating time;
   Oh, I have had enough of army life, etc.

The Girl I Left Behind Me

Lively

Traditional Fife Tune

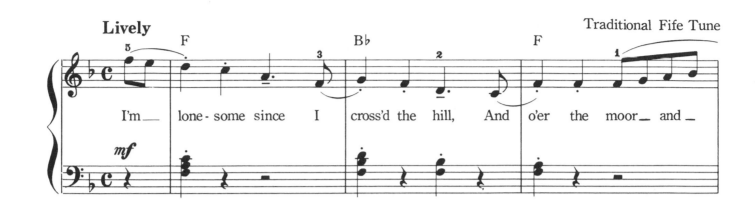

I'm_ lone - some since I cross'd the hill, And o'er the moor_ and_

val - ley; Such_ heav - y thoughts my heart do fill Since part - ing with my_

Sal - ly. I_ seek no more the fine and gay, For each but does re -

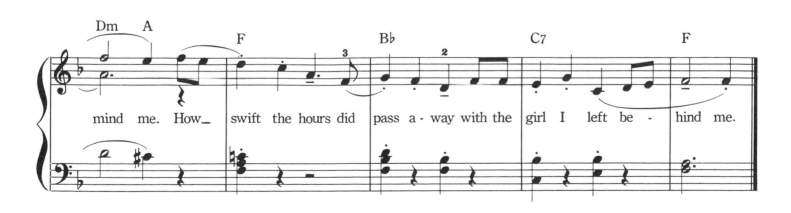

mind me. How_ swift the hours did pass a - way with the girl I left be - hind me.

Oh! Susanna

Stephen Foster

Old Folks At Home

Stephen Foster

Oh, My Darling Clementine

P. Montrose

Give Me That Old Time Religion

Spiritual

Give me that old time re - lig - ion, Give me that old time re -

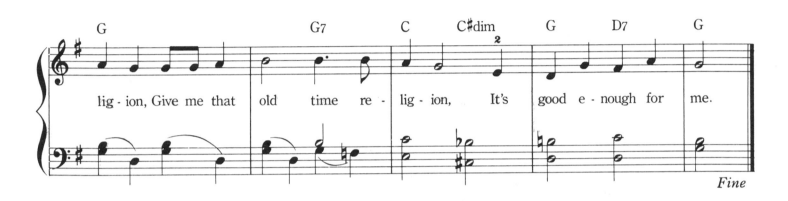

lig - ion, Give me that old time re - lig - ion, It's good e - nough for me.

Fine

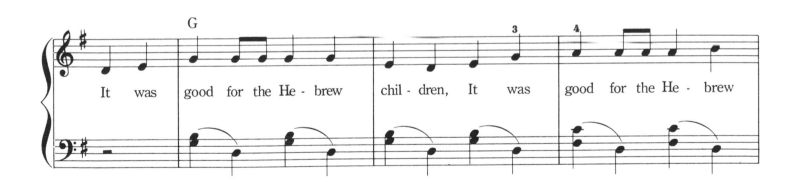

It was good for the He - brew chil - dren, It was good for the He - brew

chil - dren, It was good for the He - brew chil - dren, And it's good e - nough for me!

D.C. al Fine

Hot Time In The Old Town Tonight

Joe Hayden

T. A. Metz

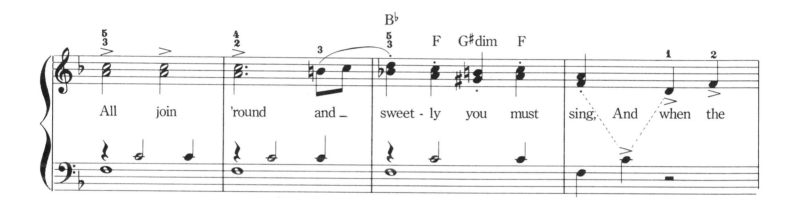

When you hear dem a bells go ding, ling, ling,

All join 'round and — sweet-ly you must sing, And when the

verse am through, in the cho-rus all join in, There'll be a

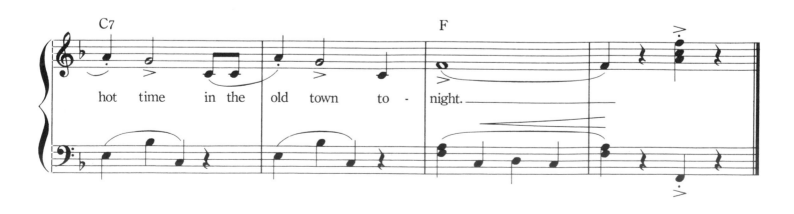

hot time in the old town to - night.

He's Got The Whole World In His Hands

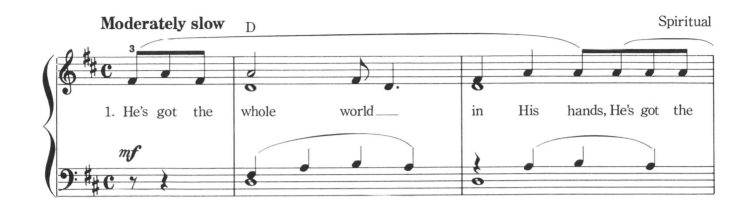

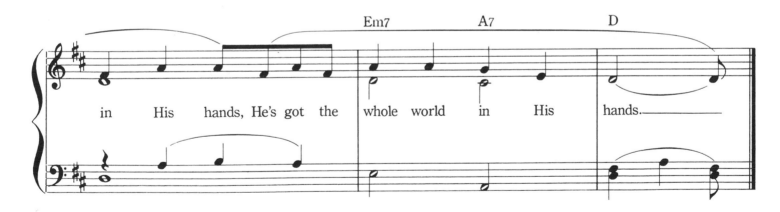

2. He's got the wind and the rain in His hands,
He's got the wind and the rain in His hands,
He's got the wind and the rain in His hands,
He's got the whole world in His hands.

3. He's got the tiny little baby in His hands,
He's got the tiny little baby in His hands,
He's got the tiny little baby in His hands,
He's got the whole world in His hands.

4. He's got you and me in His hands,
He's got you and me in His hands,
He's got you and me in His hands,
He's got the whole world in His hands.

I Ain't Gonna Grieve My Lord No More

(similarly:)

2. Oh, the deacon went down
   To the cellar to pray,
   And he got drunk,
   And stayed all day.

3. You can't get to heaven
   On roller skates,
   You'll roll right by
   Those pearly gates.

4. You can't get to heaven
   With powder and paint
   'Cause it makes you look
   Like what you ain't.

Cielito Lindo

Ted Fetter

C. Fernandez

Funiculi Funicula

Bright and happy

Luigi Denza

Some think _____ the world is made for fun and frol - ic, _____ And so do I, _____ And so do I! _____ Some think _____ it well to be all mel - an - chol - ic, _____ To pine and sigh, _____ To pine and sigh; _____ But I, _____ I love to spend my time in sing - ing _____ Some joy - ous song, _____ Some joy - ous song;

73

Come Back To Sorrento

Joseph McCarthy, Jr.

Ernesto de Curtis

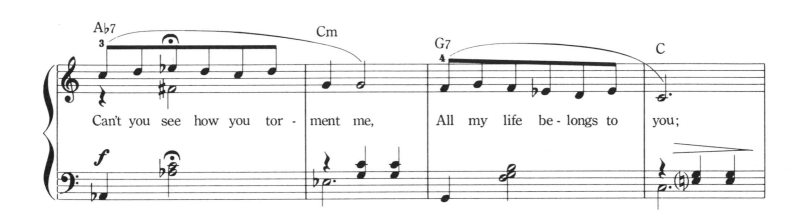

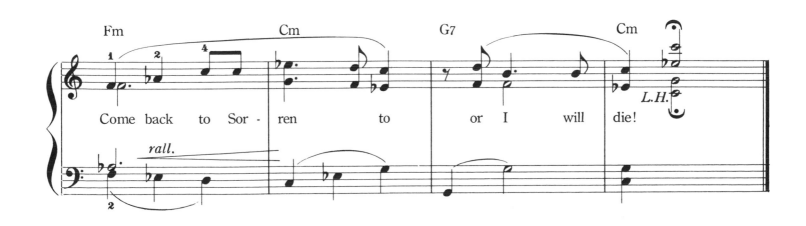

Dixie

Daniel Decatur Emmet

Bright tempo

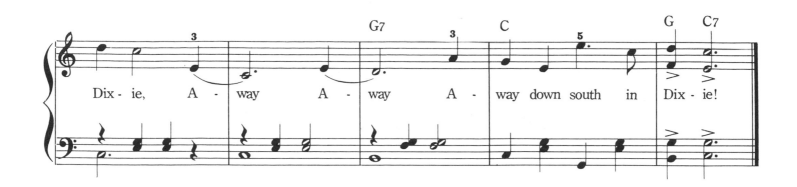

America

Samuel F. Smith

Henry Carey

Battle Hymn Of The Republic

Julia Ward Howe

Traditional

We Shall Overcome

Spiritual Song

Moderately Slow

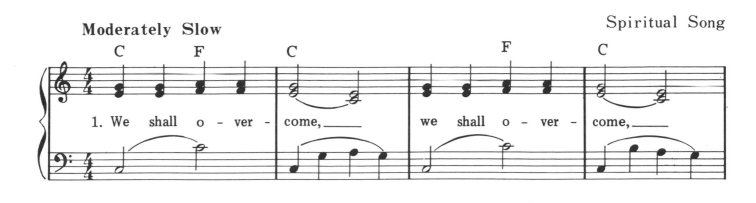

1. We shall o - ver - come,_____ we shall o - ver - come,_____

We shall o - ver - come some day._____ Oh,____

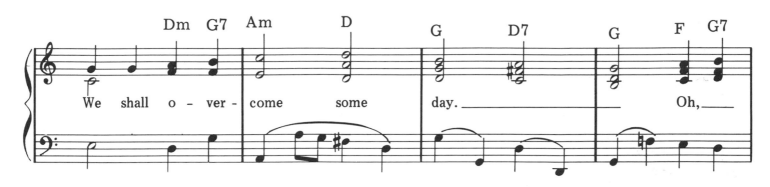

deep in my heart I do be - lieve

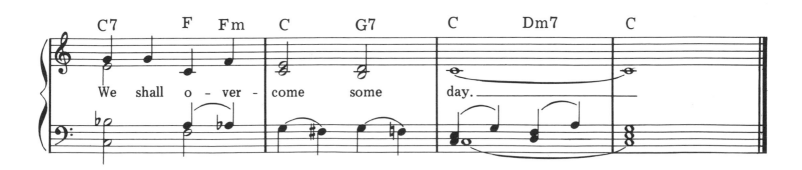

We shall o - ver - come some day._____

2. We shall walk in peace,
   We shall walk in peace,
   We shall walk in peace some day.
   Oh, deep in my heart
   I do believe
   We shall walk in peace some day.

3. We shall build a new world,
   We shall build a new world,
   We shall build a new world some day.
   Oh, deep in my heart
   I do believe
   We shall build a new world some day.

Auld Lang Syne

Scottish Air

Should auld ac-quain-tance be for-got, And ne - ver brought to mind? Should

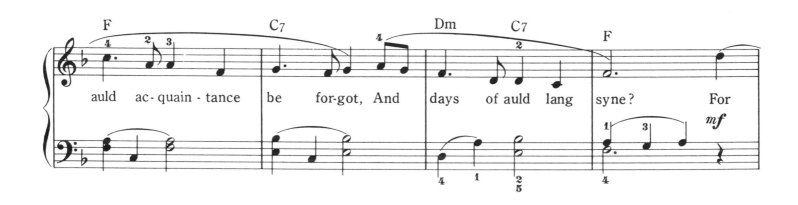

auld ac-quain-tance be for-got, And days of auld lang syne? For

auld____ lang____ syne, my dear, For auld____ lang____ syne; We'll

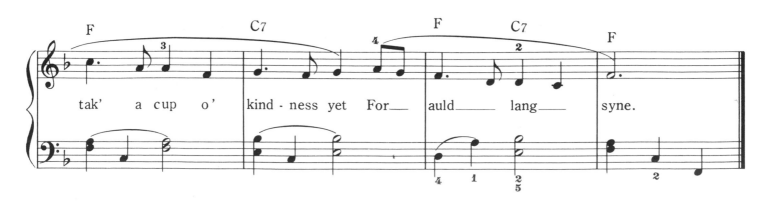

tak' a cup o' kind-ness yet For____ auld____ lang____ syne.